THE FUTURE OF SCIENCE

Bertrand Russell

THE FUTURE OF SCIENCE

With a "Self-Portrait" of the Author

WISDOM LIBRARY

A Division of
PHILOSOPHICAL LIBRARY
New York

TABLE OF CONTENTS

The Future of Science

I. INTRODUCTORY

Mr. Haldane's *Daedalus* has set forth an attractive picture of the future as it may become through the use of scientific discoveries to promote human happiness. Much as I should like to agree with his forecast, a long experience of statesmen and governments has made me somewhat sceptical. I am compelled to fear that science will be used to promote the power of dominant groups, rather than to make men happy. Icarus, having been taught to fly by his father Daedalus, was destroyed by his rashness. I fear that the same fate may overtake the populations whom modern men of science have taught to fly. Some of the dangers inherent in the progress of science while we retain our present political and economic institutions are set forth in the following pages.

This subject is so vast that it is impossible, within a limited space, to do more than outline some of its aspects. The world in which we live differs profoundly from that of Queen Anne's time, and this difference is mainly attributable to science. That is to say, the difference would be very much less than it is but for various scientific discoveries, but resulted from those discoveries by the operation of ordinary human nature. The changes that have been brought about have been partly good, partly bad; whether, in the end, science will prove to have been a blessing or a curse to mankind, is to my mind, still a doubtful question.

A science may affect human life in two different ways. On the one hand, without altering men's passions or their general outlook, it may increase their power of gratifying their desires. On the other hand, it may operate through an effect upon the imaginative conception of the world, the theology or philosophy which is accepted in practice by energetic men. The latter is a fascinating study, but I shall almost wholly ignore it in order to bring my subject within a manageable compass. I shall confine myself almost wholly to the effect of science in enabling us to gratify our passions more freely, which has hitherto been far the more important of the two.

From our point of view, we may divide

the sciences into three groups: physical, biological, and anthropological. Include chemistry, and broadly speaking any science concerned with the properties of matter apart from life. In the anthropological group I include all studies specially concerned with man: human physiology and psychology (between which no sharp line can be drawn), anthropology, history, sociology, and economics. All these studies can be illuminated by considerations drawn from biology; for instance, Rivers threw a new light on parts of economics by adducing facts about landed property among birds during the breeding season. But in spite of their connection with biology – a connection which is likely to grow closer as time goes on – they are broadly distinguished from biology by their methods and data, and deserve to be grouped apart, at any rate in a sociological inquiry.

The effect of the biological sciences, so far, has been very small. No doubt Darwinism and the idea of evolution affected men's imaginative outlook; arguments were derived in favor of free competition, and also of nationalism. But these effects were of the sort that I propose not to consider. It is probable that great effects will come from these sciences sooner or later. Mendelism might have revolutionized agriculture, and no doubt some similar theory will do so sooner or later. Bacteriology may enable us to exterminate our enemies by disease. The study of heredity may in time make eugenics an exact science, and perhaps we shall in a later age be able to determine at will the sex of our children. This would probably lead to an excess of males, involving a complete change in family institutions. But these speculations belong to the future. I do not propose to deal with the possible future effects of biology, both because my knowledge of biology is very limited, and because the subject has been admirably treated by Mr. Haldane.[1]

The anthropological sciences are those from which, *a priori*, we might have expected the greatest social effects, but hitherto this has not proved to be the case, partly because these sciences are mostly still at an early stage of development. Even economics has not so far had much effect. Where it has seemed to have, this is because it advocated what was independently desired. Hitherto, the most effective of the anthropological sciences has

---

[1] See his *Daedalus, or Science and the Future.*

been medicine, through its influence on sanitation and public health and through the fact that it has discovered how to deal with malaria and yellow fever. Birth-control is also a very important social fact which comes into this category. But although the future effect of the anthropological sciences (to which I shall return presently) is illimitable, the effect up to the present has been confined within fairly narrow limits.

One general observation to begin with. Science has increased man's control over nature, and might therefore be supposed likely to increase his happiness and well-being. This would be the case if men were rational, but in fact they are bundles of passions and instincts. An animal species in a stable environment, if it does not die out, acquires an equilibrium between its passions and the conditions of its life. If the conditions are suddenly altered, the equilibrium is upset. Wolves in a state of nature have difficulty in getting food, and therefore need the stimulus of a very insistent hunger. The result is that their descendants, domestic dogs, over-eat if they are allowed to do so. When a certain amount of something is useful, and the difficulty of obtaining it is diminished, instinct will usually lead an animal to excess in the new circumstances. The sudden change produced by science has upset the balance between our instincts and our circumstances, but in directions not sufficiently noticed. Over-eating is not a serious danger, but over-fighting is. The human instincts of power and rivalry, like the dog's wolfish appetite will need to be artificially curbed, if industrialism is to succeed.

II. EFFECTS OF THE PHYSICAL SCIENCES

Much the greatest part of the changes which science has made in social life is due to the physical sciences, as is evident when we consider that they brought about the industrial revolution. This is a trite topic, about which I shall say as little as my subject permits. There are, however, some points which must be made.

First, industrialism, still has great parts of the earth's surface to conquer. Russia and India are very imperfectly industrialized; China hardly at all. In South America there is room for immense development. One of the effects of industrialism is to make the world an economic unit: its ultimate consequences will be very largely due to this fact. But before the world can be effectively organized as a unit, it will probably be necessary to develop industrially all the regions capable of development that are at present backward. The effects of industrialism change as it becomes more wide-spread; this must be remembered in any attempt to argue from its past to its future.

The second point about industrialism is that it increases the productivity of labor, and thus makes more luxuries possible. At first, in England, the chief luxury achieved was a larger population with an actual lowering of the standard of life. Then came a golden age when wages increased, hours of labor diminished, and simultaneously the middle-class grew more prosperous. That was while Great Britain was still supreme. With the growth of foreign industrialism, a new epoch began. Industrial organizations have seldom succeeded in becoming world-wide, and have consequently become national. Competition, formerly between individual firms, is now mainly between nations, and is therefore conducted by methods quite different from those contemplated by the classical economists.

Modern industrialism is a struggle between nations for two things, markets and raw materials, as well as for the sheer pleasure of dominion. The labor which is set free from providing the necessaries of life tends to be more and more absorbed by national rivalry. There are first the armed forces of the State; then those who provide munitions of war, from the raw minerals up to the finished product; then the diplomatic and consular services;

then the teachers of patriotism in shools; then the Press. All of these perform other functions as well, but the chief purpose is to minister to international competition. As another class whose labors are devoted to the same end, we must add a considerable proportion of the men of science. These men invent continually more elaborate methods of attack and defense. The net result of their labors is to diminish the proportion of the population that can be put into the fighting line, since more are required for munitions. This might seem a boon, but in fact war is now-a-days primarily against the civilian population, and in a defeated country they are liable to suffer just as much as the soldiers.

It is science above all that has determined the importance of raw materials in international competition. Coal and iron and oil, especially, are the bases of power, and thence of wealth. The nation which possesses them, and has the industrial skill required to utilize them in war, can acquire markets by armed force, and levy tribute upon less fortunate nations. Economists have underestimated the part played by military prowess in the acquisition of wealth. The landed aristocracies of Europe were, in origin, warlike invaders. Their defeat by the bourgeoisie in the French Revolution, and the fear which this generated in the Duke of Wellington, facilitated the rise of the middle class. The wars of the eighteenth century decided that England was to be richer than France. The traditional economist's rules for the distribution of wealth hold only when men's actions are governed by law, i.e. when most people think the issue unimportant. The issues that people have considered vital have been decided by civil wars or wars between nations. And for the present, owing to science, the art of war consists in possessing coal, iron, oil, and the industrial skill to work them. For the sake of simplicity, I omit other raw materials, since they do not affect the essence of our problem.

We may say, therefore, speaking very generally, that men have used the increased productivity which they owe to science for three chief purposes in succession: first, to increase the population; then, to raise the standard of comfort; and, finally, to provide more energy to war. This last result has been chiefly brought about by competition for markets, which led to competition for raw materials, especially the raw materials of munitions.

III. THE INCREASE OF
ORGANIZATION

The stimulation of nationalism which has taken place in modern times is, however, due very largely to another factor, namely the increase of organization, which is of the very essence of industrialism. Wherever expensive fixed capital is required, organization on a large scale is of course necessary. In view of the economies of large scale production, organization in marketing also becomes of great importance. For some purposes, if not for all, many industries come to be organized nationally, so as to be in effect one business in each nation.

Science has not only brought about the need of large organizations, but also the technical possibility of their existence. Without railways, telegraphs, and telephones, control from a center is very difficult. In ancient empires, and in China down to modern times, provinces were governed by practically independent satraps or proconsuls, who were appointed by the central government, but decided almost all questions on their own initiative. If they displeased the sovereign, they could only be controlled by civil war, of which the issue was doubtful. Until the invention of the telegraph, ambassadors had a great measure of independence, since it was often necessary to act without waiting for orders from home. What applied in politics applied also in business: an organization controlled from the center had to be very loosely knit, and to allow much autonomy to subordinates. Opinion as well as action was difficult to mould from a center, and local variations marred the uniformity of party creeds.

Now-a-days all this is changed. Telegraph, telephone, and wireless make it easy to transmit orders from a center: railways and steamers make it easy to transport troops in case the orders are disobeyed. Modern methods of printing and advertising make it enormously cheaper to produce and distribute one newspaper with a large circulation than many with small circulations; consequently, in so far as the Press controls opinion, there is uniformity, and, in particular, there is uniformity of news. Elementary education, except in so far as religious denominations introduce variety, is conducted on a uniform pattern decided by the State, by means of teachers whom the State has trained, as far as possible, to imitate the regularity and mutual similarity of machines produced to standard. Thus the material and psychological conditions for a great intensity of organization have increased *pari passu*, but the basis of the whole development is scientific invention in the purely physical realm. Increased productivity has played its part, by making it possible to set apart more labor for propaganda, under which head are to be included advertisement, the cinema, the Press, education, politics, and religion. Broadcasting is a new method likely to acquire great potency as soon as people are satisfied that it is *not* a method of propaganda.

Political controversies, as Mr. Graham Wallas has pointed out, ought to be conducted in quantitative terms. If sociology were one of the sciences that had affected social institutions (which it is not), this would be the case. The dispute between anarchism and bureaucracy at present tends to take the form of one side maintaining that we want no organization, while the other maintains that we want as much as possible. A person imbued with the scientific spirit would hardly even examine these extreme positions. Some people think that we keep our rooms too hot for health, others that we keep them too cold. If this were a political question, one party would maintain that the best temperature is the absolute zero, the other that it is the melting point of iron. Those who maintained any intermediate position would be abused as timorous time-servers, concealed agents of the other side, men who maintained any intermediate position cause by tepid appeals to mere reason. Any man who had the courage to say that our rooms ought to be neither very hot nor very cold would be abused by both parties, and probably shot in No Man's Land. Possibly some day politics may become more rational but so far there is not the faintest indication of a change in this direction.

To a rational mind, the question is not: Do we want organization or do we not? The question is: How much organization do we want, and where and when and of what kind? In spite of a temperamental leaning to anarchism, I am persuaded that an industrial world cannot maintain itself against internal disruptive forces without a great deal more organization than we have at present. It is not the amount of organization, but its kind and its purposes, that cause our troubles. But before tackling this question, let us pause for a moment to ask ourselves what is the measure of the intensity of organization in a given community.

A man's acts are partly determined by spontaneous impulse, partly by the conscious or unconscious effects of the various groups to which he belongs. A man who works (say) on a railway or in a mine is, in his working-hours, almost entirely determined in his actions by those who direct the collective labor of which he forms part. If he decides to strike, his action is again not individual, but determined by his Union. When he votes for Parliament, party caucuses have limited his choice to one of two or three men, and party propaganda has induced him to accept *in toto* one of the two or three blocks of opinions which form the rival party programmes. His choice between the parties may be individual, but it may also be determined by the action of some group, such as a trade union, which collectively supports one party. His newspaper-reading exposes him to great organized forces; so does the cinema, if he goes to it. His choice of a wife is probably spontaneous, except that he must choose a woman of his own class. But in the education of his children he is almost entirely powerless: they must have the education which is provided. Organization thus determines many vital things in his life. Compare him with a handicraftsman or peasant-proprietor who cannot read and does not have his children educated, and it becomes clear what is meant by saying that industrialism has increased the intensity of organization. To define this term, we must, I think, exclude the unconscious effects of groups, except as causes facilitating the conscious effects. We may define the intensity of organization to which a given individual is subject as the proportion of his acts which is determined by the orders or advice of some group, expressed through democratic decisions or executive officers. The intensity of organization in a community may then be defined as the average intensity for its several members.

The intensity of organization is increased not only when a man belongs to more organizations, but also when the organizations to which he already belongs play a larger part in his life, as, for example, the State plays a larger part in war than in peace.

« 23 »

Another matter which needs to be treated quantitatively is the degree of democracy, oligarchy, or monarchy in an organization. No organization belongs completely to any one of the three types. There must be executive officers, who will often in practice be able to decide policy, even if in theory they cannot do so. And even if their power depends upon persuasion, they may so completely control the relevant publicity that they can always rely upon a majority. The directors of a railway company, for instance, are to all intents and purposes uncontrolled by the shareholders, who have no adequate means of organizing an opposition if they should wish to do so. In America, a railroad president is almost a monarch. In party politics, the power of leaders, although it depends upon persuasion, continually increases as printed propaganda becomes more important. For these reasons, even where formal democracy increases, the real degree of democratic control tends to diminish, except on a few questions which rouse strong popular passions.

The result of these causes is that, in consequence of scientific inventions which facilitate centralization and propaganda, groups become more organized, more disciplined, more group-conscious, and more docile to leaders. The effect of leaders on followers is increased, and the control of events by a few prominent personalities becomes more marked.

In all this there would be nothing very tragic, but for the fact, with which science has nothing to do, that organization is almost wholly national. If men were actuated by the love of gain, as the older economists supposed, this would not be the case; the same causes which have led to national trusts would have led to international trusts. This has happened in a few instances, but not on a sufficiently wide scale to affect politics or economics very vitally. Rivalry is, with most well-to-do energetic people, a stronger motive than love of money. Successful rivalry requires organization of rival forces; the tendency is for a business such as oil, for example, to organize itself into two rival groups, between them covering the world. They might, of course, combine, and they would no doubt increase their wealth if they did so. But combination would take the zest out of life. The object of a football team, one might say, is to kick goals. If two rival teams combined, and kicked

the ball alternately over the two goals,
many more goals would be scored. Nevertheless no one suggests that this should be
done, the object of a football team being
not to kick goals but to win. So the object
of a big business is not to make money,
but to win in the contest with some other
business. If there were no other business
to be defeated, the whole thing would become uninteresting. This rivalry has at-
tached itself to nationalism, and enlisted
the support of the ordinary citizens of the
countries concerned; they seldom know
what it is that they are supporting, but,
like the spectators at a football-match,
they grow enthusiastic for their own side.
The harm that is being done by science
and industrialism is almost wholly due to
the fact that, while they have proved
strong enough to produce a *national*

organization of economic forces, they have not proved strong enough to produce an international organization. It is clear that political internationalism such as the League of Nations was supposed to inaugurate, will never be successful until we have economic internationalism, which would require, as a minimum, an agreement between various national organizations dividing among them the raw materials and markets of the world. This, however, can hardly be brought about while big business is controlled by men who are so rich as to have grown indifferent to money, and to be willing to risk enormous losses for the pleasure of rivalry.

The increase of organization in the modern world has made the ideals of liberalism wholly inapplicable. Liberalism, from Montesquieu to President Wilson, was based upon the assumption of a number of more or less equal individuals or groups, with no differences so vital that they were willing to die sooner than compromise. It was supposed that there was to be free competition between individuals and between ideas. Experience has shown, however, that the existing economic system is incompatible with all forms of free competition except between States by means of armaments. I should wish, for my part, to preserve free competition between ideas, though not between individuals and groups, but this is only possible by means of what an old-fashioned liberal would regard as interferences with personal liberty. So long as the sources of economic power remain in private hands, there will be no liberty except for the few who control those sources.

Such liberal ideals as free trade, free press, unbiased education, either already belong to the past or soon will do so. One of the triumphs of early liberalism in England was the establishment of parliamentary control over the army; this was the *casus belli* in the Civil War, and was decided by the Revolution of 1688. It was effective so long as Parliament represented the same class from which army officers were drawn. This was still the case with the late Parliament, but may cease to be the case with the advent of a Labor Government. Russia, Hungary, Italy, Spain, and Bavaria have shown in recent years how frail democracy has become; east of the Rhine it lingers only in outlying regions. Constitutional control over armaments must, therefore, be regarded as another liberal principle which is rapidly becoming obsolete.

It would seem probable that, in the next fifty years or so, we shall see a still further increase in the power of governments, and a tendency for governments to be such as are desired by the men who control armaments and raw materials. The forms of democracy may survive in western countries, since those who possess military and economic power can control education and the press, and therefore can usually secure a subservient democracy. Rival economic groups will presumably remain associated with rival nations, and will foster nationalism in order to recruit their football teams.

There is, however, a hopeful element in the problem. The planet is of finite size, but the most efficient size for an organization is continually increased by new scientific inventions. The world becomes more and more of an economic unity. Before very long the technical conditions will exist for organizing the whole world as one producing and consuming unit. If, when that time comes, two rival groups contend for mastery, the victor may be able to introduce that single world-wide organization that is needed to prevent the mutual extermination of civilized nations. The world which would result would be, at first, very different from the dreams of either liberals or socialists; but it might grow less different with the lapse of time. There would be at first economic and political tryanny of the victors, a dread of renewed upheavals, and therefore a drastic suppression of liberty. But

if the first half-dozen revolts were success-
fully repressed, the vanquished would
give up hope, and accept the subordinate
place assigned to them by the victors in
the great world-trust. As soon as the
holders of power felt secure, they would
grow less tyrannical and less energetic.
The motive of rivalry being removed, they
would not work so hard as they do now,
and would soon cease to exact such hard
work from their subordinates. Life at first
might be unpleasant, but it would at least
be possible, which would be enough to
recommend the system after a long period
of warfare. Given a stable world-organ-
ization, economic and political, even if,
at first, it rested upon nothing but armed
force, the evils which now threaten civilization would gradually diminish, and a
more thorough democracy than that

which now exists might become possible. I believe that, owing to men's folly, a world-government will only be established by force, and will therefore be at first cruel and depotic. But I believe that it is necessary for the preservation of a scientific civilization, and that, if once realized, it will gradually give rise to the other conditions of a tolerable existence.

IV. THE ANTHROPOLOGICAL SCIENCES

It remans to say something about the effects of the anthropological sciences. This is of course extremely conjectural, because we do not know what discoveries will be made. The effect is likely to be far greater than we can now imagine, because these sciences are still in their infancy. I will, however, take a few points on which to hang conjectures. I do not wish to be supposed to be making prophecies: I am only suggesting possibilities which it may be instructive to consider.

Birth-control is a matter of great importance, particularly in relation to the possibility of a world-government, which could hardly be stable if some nations increased their population much more rapidly than others. At present, birth-control is increasing in all civilized countries, though in most it is opposed by governments. This opposition is due partly to mere superstition and desire to conciliate the Catholic vote, partly to the desire for large armies and severe competition between wage-earners, so as to keep down wages. In spite of the opposition of governments, it seems probable that birth-control will lead to a stationary population in most white nations within the next fifty years. There can be no security that it will stop with a stationary population; it may go on to the point where the population diminishes.

The increase in the practice of birth-control is an example of a process contrary to that seen in industrialism: it represents a victory of individual over collective passions. Collectively, Frenchmen desire that France should be populous, in order to be able to defeat her enemies in war. Individually, they desire that their own families should be small, in order to increase the inheritance of their children and to diminish the expense of education. The individual desire has triumphed over the collective desire, and even, in many cases, over religious scruples. In this case, as in most others, the individual desire is less harmful to the world than the collective desire: the man who acts from pure selfishness does less damage than the man who is actuated by "public spirit." For, since medicine and sanitation have diminished the infant death-rate, the only checks to over-population that remain (apart from birth-control) are war and famine. So long as this continues to be the case, the world must either have a nearly stationary population, or employ war to produce famine. The latter method, which is that favored by opponents of birth-control, has been adopted on a large scale since 1914; it is however somewhat wasteful. We require a certain number of cattle and sheep, and we take steps to secure the right number. If we were as indifferent about them as we are about human beings, we should produce far too many, and cause the surplus to die by the slow misery of under-feeding. Farmers would consider this plan extravagant, and humanitarians would consider it cruel. But where human beings are concerned, it is considered the only proper course, and works advocating any other are confiscated by the police if they are intelligible to those whom they concern.

It must be admitted, however, that there are certain dangers. Before long the population may actually diminish. This is already happening in the most intelligent sections of the most intelligent nations; government opposition to birth-control propaganda gives a biological advantage to stupidity, since it is chiefly stupid people whom governments succeed in keeping in ignorance. Before long, birth-control may become nearly universal among the white races; it will then not deteriorate their quality, but only diminish their numbers, at a time when uncivilized races are still prolific and are preserved from a high death-rate by white science.

This situation will lead to a tendency – already shown by the French – to employ more prolific races as mercenaries. Governments will oppose the teaching of birth-control among Africans, for fear of losing recruits. The result will be an immense numerical inferiority of the white races, leading probably to their extermination in a mutiny of mercenaries. If, however, a world-government is established, it may see the desirability of making subject races also less prolific, and may permit mankind to solve the population question. This is another reason for desiring a world-government.

Passing from quantity to quality of population, we come to the question of eugenics. We may perhaps assume that, if people grow less superstitious, governments will acquire the right to sterilize those who are not considered desirable as parents. This power will be used, at first, to diminish imbecility, a most desirable object. But probably, in time, opposition to the government will be taken to prove imbecility, so that rebels of all kinds will be sterilized. Epileptics, consumptives, dipsomaniacs and so on will gradually be included; in the end, there will be a tendency to include all who fail to pass the usual school examinations. The result will be to increase the average intelligence; in the long run, it may be greatly increased. But probably the effect upon really exceptional intelligence will be bad. Mr. Micawber, who was Dickens's father, would hardly have been regarded as a desirable parent. How many imbeciles ought to outweigh one Dickens I do not profess to know.

Eugenics has, of course, more ambitious possibilities in a more distant future. It may aim not only at eliminating undesired types. Moral standards may alter so as to make it possible for one man to be the sire of a vast progeny by many different mothers. When men of science envisage a possibility of this kind, they are prone to a type of fallacy which is common also in other directions. They imagine that a reform inaugurated by men of science would be administered as men of science would wish, by men similar in outlook to those who have advocated it. In like manner women who advocated votes for women used to imagine that the woman voter of the future would resemble the ardent feminist who won her the vote; and socialist leaders imagine that a socialist State would be administered by idealistic reformers like themselves. These are, of course, delusions; a reform, once achieved, is handed over to the average citizen. So, if eugenics reached the point where it could increase desired types, it would not be the types desired by present-day eugenists that would be increased, but rather the types desired by the average official. Prime Ministers, Bishops, and others whom the State considers desirable might become the fathers of half the next generation. Whether this would be an improvement it is not for me to say, as I

have no hope of ever becoming either a
Bishop or a Prime Minister.

If we knew enough about heredity to
determine, within limits, what sort of population we would have, the matter would
of course be in the hands of State officials,
presumably elderly medical men. Whether
they would really be preferable to Nature
I do not feel sure. I suspect that they
would breed a subservient population,
convenient to rulers but incapable of initiative. However, it may be that I am too
sceptical of the wisdom of officials.

The effects of psychology on practical
life may in time become very great. Already advertisers in America employ emi-
nent psychologists to instruct them in the
technique of producing irrational belief;
such men may, when they have grown
more proficient, be very useful in per-

suading the democracy that governments are wise and good. Then, again, there are the psychological tests of intelligence, as applied to recruits for the American army during the war. I am very sceptical of the possibility of testing anything except average intelligence by such methods, and I think that, if they were widely adopted, they would probably lead to many persons of great artistic capacity being classified as morons. The same thing would have happened to some first-rate mathematicians. Specialized ability not infrequently goes with general disability, but this would not be shown by the kind of tests which psychologists recommended to the American government.

More sensational than tests of intelligence is the possibility of controlling the emotional life through the secretions of the ductless glands. It will be possible to make people choleric or timid, strongly or weakly sexed, and so on, as may be desired. Differences of emotional disposition seem to be chiefly due to secretions of the ductless glands, and therefore controllable by injections or by increasing or diminishing the secretions. Assuming an oligarchic organization of society, the State could give to the children of holders of power the disposition required for command, and to the children of the proletariat the disposition required for obedience. Against the injections of the State physicians the most eloquent Socialist oratory would be powerless. The only difficulty would be to combine this submissiveness with the necessary ferocity against external enemies; but I do not doubt that official science would be equal to the task.

It is not necessary, when we are considering political consequences, to pin our faith to the particular theories of the ductless glands, which may blow over, like other theories. All that is essential in our hypothesis is the belief that physiology will in time find ways of controlling emotion, which it is scarcely possible to doubt. When that day comes, we shall have the emotions desired by our rulers, and the chief business of elementary education will be to produce the desired disposition, no longer by punishment or moral precept, but by the far surer method of injection or diet. The man who will administer this system will have a power beyond the dreams of the Jesuits, but there is no reason to suppose that they will have more sense than the men who control education to-day. Technical scientific knowledge does not make men sensible in their aims, and administrators in the future will be presumably no less stupid and no less prejudiced than they are at present.

CONCLUSION

It may seem as though I had been at once gloomy and frivolous in some of my prognostications. I will end, however, with the serious lesson which seems to me to result. Men sometimes speak as though the progress of science must necessarily be a boon to mankind, but that, I fear, is one of the comfortable nineteenth-century delusions which our more disillusioned age must discard. Science enables the holders of power to realize their pur-

poses more fully than they could otherwise do. If their purposes are good, this is
a gain; if they are evil, it is a loss. In the
present age, it seems that the purposes of
the holders of power are in the main evil,
in the sense that they involve a diminu-
tion, in the world at large, of the things
men are agreed in thinking good. Therefore, at present, science does harm by increasing the power of rulers. Science is
no substitute for virtue; the heart is as
necessary for a good life as the head.

If men were rational in their conduct,
that is to say, if they acted in the way
most likely to bring about the ends that
they deliberately desire, intelligence would
be enough to make the world almost a
paradise. In the main, what is in the long
run advantageous to one man is also advantageous to another. But men are actu-

ated by passions which distort their view; feeling an impulse to injure others, they persuade themselves that it is to their interest to do so. They will not, therefore, act in the way which is in fact to their own interest unless they are actuated by generous impulses which make them indifferent to their own interest. This is why the heart is as important as the head. By the "heart" I mean, for the moment, the sum-total of kindly impulses. Where they exist, science helps them to be effective; where they are absent, science only makes men more cleverly diabolic.

It may be laid down as a general principle to which there are few exceptions that, when people are mistaken as to what is to their own interest, the course they believe to be wise is more harmful to others than the course that really is wise. There are innumerable examples of men making fortunes because, on moral grounds, they did something which they believed to be contrary to their own interests. For instance, among early Quakers there were a number of shopkeepers, who adopted the practice of asking no more for their goods than they were willing to accept, instead of bargaining with each customer, as everybody else did. They adopted this practice because they held it to be a lie to ask more than they would take. But the convenience to customers was so great that everybody came to their shops and they grew rich. (I forget where I read this, but if my memory serves me it was in some reliable source.) The same policy *might* have been adopted from shrewdness but in fact no one was sufficiently shrewd. Our unconscious is more malevolent than it pays us to be; therefore the people who do most completely what is in fact to their interest are those who, on moral grounds, do what they believe to be against their interest.

For this reason, it is of the greatest importance to inquire whether any method of strengthening kindly impulses exists. I have no doubt that their strength or weakness depends upon discoverable physiological causes; let us assume that it depends upon the glands. If so, an international secret society of physiologists could bring about the millennium by kidnapping, on a given day, all the rulers of the world, and injecting into their blood some substance which would fill them with benevolence towards their fellow-creatures. Suddenly M. Poincaré would wish well to Ruhr miners, Lord Curzon to Indian nationalists, Mr. Smuts to the natives of what was German South West Africa, the American Government to its political prisoners and its victims in Ellis Island. But alas, the physiologists would first have to administer the love-philtre to themselves before they would undertake such a task. Otherwise, they would prefer to win titles and fortunes by injecting military ferocity into recruits. And so we come back to the old dilemma: only kindliness can save the world, and even if we knew how to produce kindliness we should not do so unless we were already kindly. Failing that, it seems that the solution which the Houynhnms adopted towards the Yahoos, namely extermination, is the only one; apparently the Yahoos are bent on applying it to each other.

We may sum up this discussion in a

few words. Science has not given men more self-control, more kindliness, or more power of discounting their passions in deciding upon a course of action. It has given communities more power to indulge their collective passions, but, by making society more organic, it has diminished the part played by private passions. Men's collective passions are mainly evil; far the strongest of them are hatred and rivalry directed towards other groups. Therefore at present all that gives men power to indulge their collective passions is bad. That is why science threatens to cause the destruction of our civilization. The only solid hope seems to lie in the possibility of world-wide domination by one group, say the United States, leading to the gradual formation of an orderly economic and political world-government.

But perhaps, in view of the sterility of the
Roman Empire, the collapse of our civilization would in the end be preferable to
this alternative.

"Self-Portrait"
of the Author

I wrote in 1937 a prophecy of what I
thought The Times would say about me
when I died. The obituary said:

"By the death of the third Earl Russell,
or Bertrand Russell as he preferred to
call himself, at the age of ninety, a link
with a very distant past is severed. His
grandfather, Lord John Russell, the Vic-
torian Prime Minister, visited Napoleon
in Elba; his maternal grandmother was a
friend of the Young Pretender's widow.

In his youth he did work of importance in mathematical logic, but his eccentric attitude during the first World War revealed a lack of balanced judgment which increasingly infected his later writings.

"In the second World War he took no public part, having escaped to a neutral country just before its outbreak. In private conversation he was wont to say that homicidal lunatics were well employed in killing each other, but that sensible men would keep out of their way while they were doing it. Fortunately this outlook, which is reminiscent of Bentham, has become rare in this age, which recognizes that heroism has a value independent of its utility.

"True, much of what was once the civilized world lies in ruins, but no right thinking person can admit that those who died for the right in the great struggle have died in vain.

"His life, for all its waywardness, had a certain anachronistic consistency, reminiscent of that of the aristocratic rebels of the early nineteenth century. His principles were curious, but such as they were they governed his actions. In private life he showed none of the acerbity which marred his writings, but was a genial conversationalist, not devoid of human sympathy. He had many friends but has survived almost all of them. Nevertheless to those who remained he appeared in extreme old age full of enjoyment, no doubt owing in large measure to his invariable health, for politically during his last years he was as isolated as Milton after the Restoration. He was the last survivor of a dead epoch."

I observe that the date I attributed to my death is 1962, which is coming ominously near, and begins to cause me some alarm.

Freeman: Well, before you feel too much alarmed, let us examine this obituary which was written in jest and see how true it really is. To start with, let's go back to the distant past. What is your very earliest memory, Lord Russell?

Russell: I suppose my very earliest memory is tumbling out of a pony carriage when I was two years old, and my earliest at all vivid memories are of arriving at the house of my grandparents, Pembroke Lodge, in Richmond Park, after

---

* John Freeman is the B.B.C. correspondent who conducted this interview.

the death of my father, who died when I was three.

Freeman: How did you come to be in the care of your grandparents? Your mother had also died?

Russell: Yes, she also. She died when I was two.

Freeman: Do you have any memory of your parents?

Russell: Very little. I remember nothing of my mother. I remember my father once giving me a leaflet printed in red letters, and the red letters pleased me.

* * *

Freeman: Were you always a skeptic

from small childhood or did you believe in the conventions?

Russell: Oh, I wasn't a skeptic when I was very young, no. I was very deeply religious and lost my conventional beliefs very slowly and painfully. I remember that when I was four years old they had just been telling me the story of little Red Ridinghood, and I dreamed that I had been eaten by a wolf, and to my great surprise I was in the wolf's stomach and not in heaven.

Freeman: This was the beginning perhaps of skepticism?

Russell: Yes.

Freeman: Tell me, did you say your

prayers when you were a child?

Russell: Oh, yes.

Freeman: When did you cease doing that?

Russell: I suppose when I was about twelve or thirteen.

Freeman: Do you think now that you had a happy childhood?

Russell: More or less. It was very solitary. I had one brother who was seven years older than me and I had little to do with him. Otherwise I didn't have much to do with other children, so that it was a solitary childhood, but it was not unhappy.

Freeman: Looking back now, with all the learning that you have acquired since, would you say that some feeling of insecurity was one of the spurs to intellectual action?

Russell: I don't quite know. I think it's a possible spur. I think there are others of a different sort; pure ambition will sometimes do it.

Freeman: Were you obsessed at a tender age with a sense of guilt or sin?

Russell: Oh, yes. They asked me one day what was my favorite hymn and I chose 'Weary of earth and laden with my sin.'

Freeman: At what age was that?

Russell: Six years old. The things I felt guilty about were – oh, eating blackberries when I had been told not to, and I remember once when at family prayers my grandmother read about the prodigal son, I said to her afterwards: "I know why you read that today: it was because I broke my jug."

Freeman: Do you think now, looking back, that there is any really unfortunate legacy you carried out of your childhood?

Russell: Yes, I do. The family attitude, certainly on matters of sex, was morbidly puritanical.

Freeman: Now, let us turn to your schooling.

Russell: My grandmother didn't approve of public schools. She was very unconventional in her outlook, and she thought they were a sort of conventional institution.

Freeman: Would you have liked a more conventional education?

Russell: No, not at the time. I was quite satisfied, and I think looking back I'm still satisfied, because I learned a great deal more than I should have done at any school.

Freeman: What sort of learning, at that age? Did you, for instance, study the classics?

Russell: To a certain degree. I was

never fond of the classics. Mathematics was what I liked. My first lesson in mathematics I had from my brother, who started me on Euclid, and I thought it the most lovely stuff I'd ever seen in my life. I didn't know there was anything so nice in the world. But I remember that the first lesson was a disappointment because he said: "Now, we start with axioms." I said: "What are they?" and he said: "Oh, they're things you've got to admit although we can't prove them." So I said: "Why should I admit them if you can't prove them?" and he said: "Well, if you won't we can't go on." And I wanted to see how it went on, so I admitted them *pro tem*.

Freeman: How did you educate your own children?

Russell: I educated them in various ways: I tried to find modern schools, but I think that there are some things in what's called progressive education that I like and some that I don't like; and I never found exactly what I should like.

Freeman: Did you send any of your own children to an ordinary public school?

Russell: Yes, my youngest son went to Eton.

Freeman: And was that successful?

Russell: Yes, quite successful.

Freeman: What was it that first provided you with the incentive to become a mathematician?

Russell: I liked it for a number of reasons: in the first place, the sheer pleasure which is the sort that people get from music or poetry – it just delighted me. And then, apart from that, I thought that mathematics was the key to understanding the universe, and I found all sorts of everyday things explained by means of mathematics. I remember I had a new tutor once who didn't know how much I knew, and I spun a penny, and he said: 'Do you know why that penny spins?' I said: 'Yes, because I make a couple with my fingers,' and he said: 'What do you know about couples?' I said: 'Oh, I know all about couples!'

Freeman: How old were you then?

« **67** »

Russell: I must have been twelve or thirteen.

Freeman: Have you found on the whole in your own life that the pursuit of either mathematics or philosophy has given you some sort of substitute for religious emotion?

Russell: Yes, it certainly has. Until I was about forty, I should think. I got the sort of satisfaction that Plato says you can get out of mathematics. It was an eternal world, it was a timeless world, it was a world where there was a possibility of a certain kind of perfection, and I certainly got something analogous to religious satisfaction out of it.

Freeman: What period of your life, or

rather what episode in your life, led you to turn again from philosophy, to some extent, into social work and politics?

Russell: The first war. The first war made me think 'It just won't do to live in an ivory tower. This world is too bad. We must notice it.' I thought, as a politician, and I still think, that it would have been very much better for the world if Britain had remained neutral and the Germans had won a quick victory. We should not have had either the Nazis or the Communists if that had happened, because they were both products of the first World War. The war would have been brief; there would have been nothing like so much destruction.

Freeman: Have you ever had a moral

objection in principle to killing?

Russell: Oh, no. I don't like any kind of general rule like that.

Freeman: How much in fact did you actively campaign against the first World War?

Russell: As much as I could. I went all over the place, making speeches, and I did everything I could to help the conscientious objectors. I wrote about it wherever I could.

Freeman: Did you have a sort of public notoriety as an unpopular figure or were you regarded as just a crank?

Russell: I wasn't actually pelted with rotten eggs, but I had an almost worse experience. I was at a meeting of pacifists at a church and it was stormed by a mixture of colonial troops and drunken viragos. The drunken viragos came in bearing boards full of rusty nails, with which they clamped everybody on the head, and the colonial soldiers looked on and applauded them, and the police looked on and did nothing. Women had all their clothes torn off their back and were badly mauled, and the viragos with rusty nails were just about to attack me – I didn't quite know what one did about this – when somebody went up to the police and said: 'Look, you really ought to stop these women, you know, he's a distinguished writer.' 'Oh,' said the police. 'Yes, he's a well-known phil-osopher.' 'Oh,' said the police. '*And he's the brother of an earl!*' And then the police rushed and saved me.

Freeman: Was this the time that you went to prison?

Russell: No, this was earlier.

Freeman: What exactly did you go to prison for?

Russell: For writing an article. I was convicted on the ground that this article was 'intended and likely to cause bad relations between England and the United States,' because I pointed out how United States troops were used as strike-breakers and it was thought I oughtn't to have done that.

Freeman: Were you tried by a jury or by a magistrate?

Russell: By a magistrate in London. And he said this was 'the most despicable crime.' He sentenced me to six months. Originally it was six months as an ordinary criminal, and then on appeal it was altered to six months in the First Division.

Freeman: Which meant more lenient treatment?

Russell: Oh, very much. It's a profound difference.

Freeman: Do you think, looking back, that Trinity College behaved either wisely or justly in depriving you of your Fellowship at the time of your own trial and imprisonment?

Russell: No, certainly not, especially
as they did it while the case was *sub judice*.
You see, all the younger Fellows had gone
to war and the government of the college
was left to the old boys, and the old boys
said, 'We must do our bit – we can't fight,
we're too old,' and their bit was to get rid
of me!

Freeman: Something very similar to
that, of course, happened in the second
World War, when your appointment at
the College of the City of New York was
terminated. What actually did happen?

Russell: Oh, in the second World War
I was completely patriotic, I supported the
war, and I was entirely orthodox in my
views about that.

Feeman: Nevertheless you were thrown out of another college?

Russell: Ah, but that was for quite different reasons. That was on the ground of my views about marriage and morals.

Freeman: But your views must have been known when you were appointed to the College of the City of New York?

Russell: Oh, yes. Civilized people didn't mind them, but there was a whole rabble in New York of uneducated Irish people, and they had completely ignorant views.

Freeman: What happened to you when you lost your job in New York? Did you have another job to go to in America?

Russell: I didn't know I should have. I was completely ostracized. No newspaper would print a word I wrote, no magazine would print a word, no hall would allow me to lecture in it, so that I was cut off from all my means of livelihood, and I couldn't get any money out of England at that time because of currency regulations, and so I was expecting to starve. I had three children whom I was educating, two of them at the university and one younger, and I expected we should all suffer very badly; and we should have done but for a certain man called Dr. Barnes who came to my rescue and gave me a job.

Freeman: Is that the only time in your life that you've ever been really short of money?

Russell: Most of my life I've only had just enough, and the rest of my life I've generally had just enough with a certain security; but at that time I really did not know how I was going to carry on my children's education.

Freeman: Could I ask you, because it's of interest to the background of the academic life generally, were you left a fortune by your family, or have you earned all you've had all your life?

Russell: I was left a certain amount of money. When I came of age I had capital that brought me in about £ 600 a year, and then I became a socialist and I came to the conclusion that I ought not to live on inherited money, and I got rid of my capital gradually to various causes which

I thought important. Since then I've lived entirely on my earnings.

Freeman: Looking back now on all the causes that you have especially championed throughout your working life, do you think your advocacy has been on the whole successful?

Russell: It depends entirely upon what things you're thinking of. My views on what you may call sexual questions have, I think, been immensely successful – I mean, the world has moved that way; and to a very great extent on education, too. And one of the things that I used to be enormously interested in was equality of women, and that of course has been completely successful. Also I was from an early time a socialist and there is a great deal of socialism in England now and I'm glad of it. So that I have had a fair measure of success; but in other things of course not at all.

Freeman: Do you think that on the whole the fanatics in the world are more useful or more dangerous than the skeptics?

Russell: Oh, much more dangerous. Fanaticism is *the* danger of the world, and always has been, and has done untold harm. I might almost say that I was fanatical against fanaticism.

Freeman: But then are you not fanatical also against some other things? Your current campaign, for instance, in favor of nuclear disarmament – would you encourage your supporters to undertake some of the extreme demonstrations that they do undertake and isn't that fanaticism?

Russell: I don't think that's fanaticism, no. I mean, some of them may be fanatical, but I support them because everything sane and sensible and quiet that we do is absolutely ignored by the press, and the only way we can get into the press is to do something that looks fanatical. The worst possibility is that human life may be extinguished, and it is a very real possibility; but assuming that doesn't happen, I can't bear the thought of many hundreds of millions of people dying in agony, solely because the rulers of the world are stupid and wicked.

Freeman: Is it true or untrue that in recent years you advocated that a preventive war might be made against communism, against Soviet Russia?

Russell: It's entirely true, and I don't repent of it. It was not inconsistent with what I think now. What I thought all along was that a nuclear war in which both sides had nuclear weapons would be an utter and absolute disaster. There was a time, just after the last war, when the Americans had a monopoly of nuclear weapons and offered to internationalize nuclear weapons by the Baruch proposal, and I thought this an extremely generous proposal on their part, one which it would be very desirable that the world should accept; not that I advocated a nuclear war, but I did think that great pressure should be put upon Russia to accept the Baruch proposal, and I did think that if they continued to refuse it might be necessary actually to go to war. At that time nuclear weapons existed only on one side, and therefore the odds were the Russians would have given way. I thought they would, and I think still that could have prevented the existence of two equal powers with these means of destruction, which is what is causing the terrible risk now.

Freeman: Suppose they hadn't given way, would you have been prepared to face the consequences? You would have used these weapons on the Russians in spite of the words you have used to me about their horror?

Russell: I should. They were not, of course, nearly as bad as these modern weapons are. They hadn't yet got the hydrogen bomb, they had only the atom bomb (and that's bad enough, but it isn't anything like the hydrogen bomb). I thought then, and hoped, that the Russians would give way, but of course you can't threaten unless you're prepared to have your bluff called.

Freeman: Do you look back to the nineteenth century on the whole with nostalgia and regret?

Russell: It all depends on what you're thinking about. The world was much more beautiful to look at than it is now. Every time I go back to a place that I knew long ago I think how sad it is. One piece of beauty after another is destroyed, and that I do profoundly regret. But when it comes to ideas, there's immensely less humbug than there was, and that I rejoice in.

Freeman: Have you written an auto-biography?

Russell: I have, yes.

Freeman: Are you going to allow it to be published in your lifetime?

Russell: No, not till I'm dead. In the first place because it won't be complete until then, and in the second place because there are all sorts of things that ought not to be said too soon. It may even have to wait some time after I'm dead – I don't know.

Freeman: One last question: suppose, Lord Russell, that this film were to be looked at by your descendants in 1,000 years' time, what would you think it worth telling that generation about the life you've lived and the lessons you've learned from it?

Russell: I should like to say two things, one intellectual and one moral. The intellectual thing I should want to say to them is this: when you are studying any matter or considering any philosophy, ask yourself only what are the facts and what is the truth that the facts bear out. Never let yourself be diverted either by what you would wish to believe or by what you think would have beneficent social effects if it were believed. But look only at what are the facts. The moral thing I should wish to say to them is very simple. I should say love is wise, hatred is foolish. In this world, which is getting more and more closely interconnected, we have to learn to put up with the fact that some people say things that we don't like. We can only live together in that way and if we are to live together and not die together we must learn a kind of charity and a kind of tolerance which is absolutely vital to the continuance of human life on this planet.